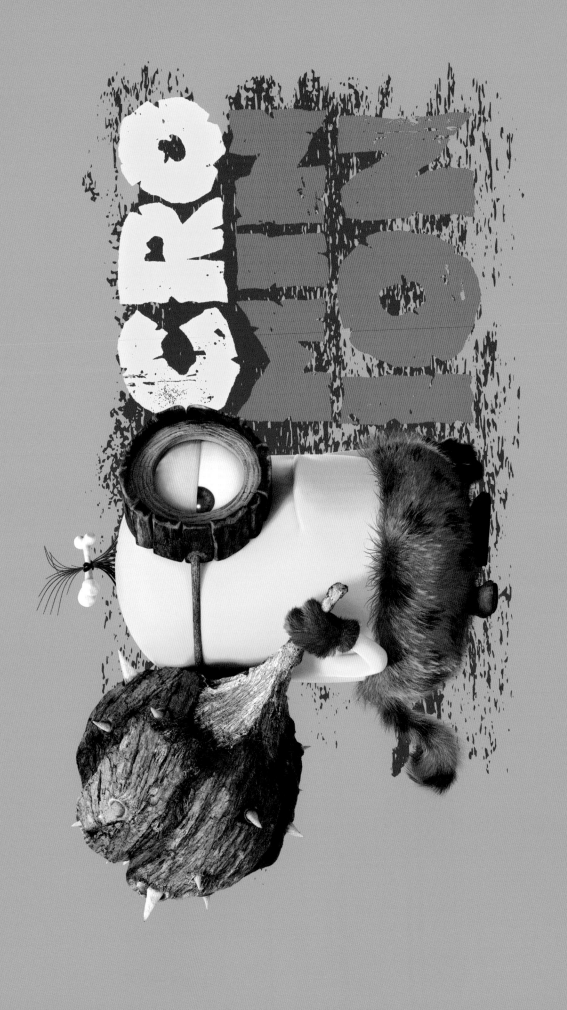

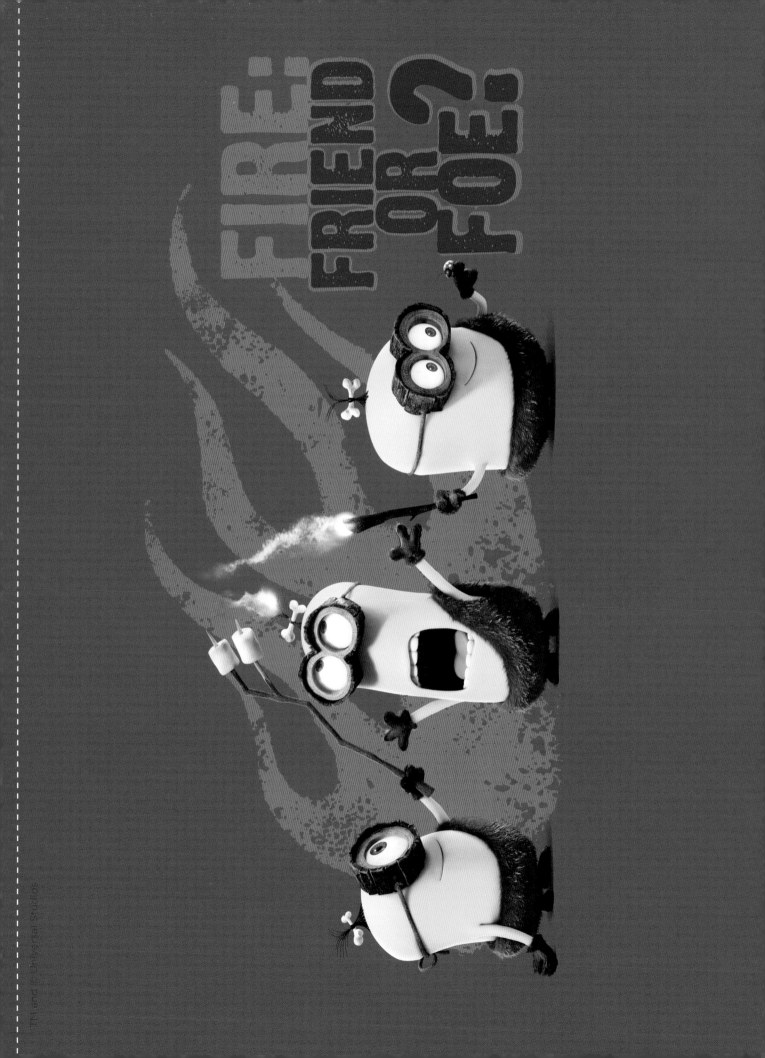

FIRE: FRIEND OR FOE?

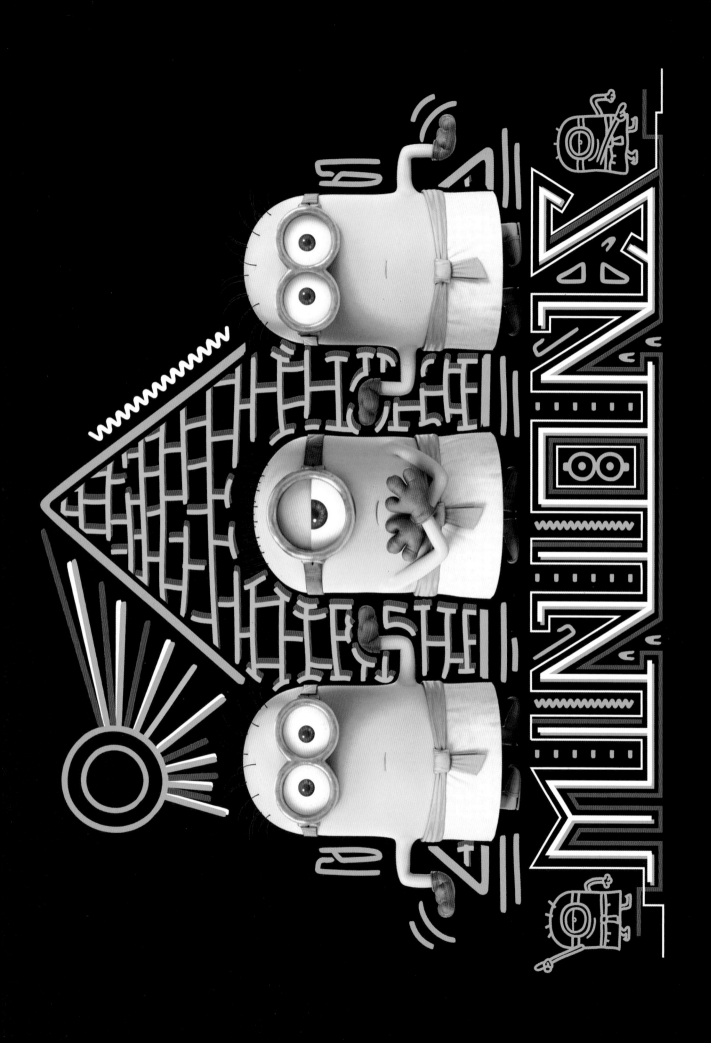

TRÈS TRÈS *Cute*

ONE IN A
MINION

PROUD TO BE A

MINION

KEEP
CALM
AND
POTAKINO
LO PATATA

TRANSLATION·YAY. EVIL

KEEP
CALM
AND
EAT A
BANANA

KEEP
STUART
VERY
CALM

BOB

STUART

KEVIN

minions

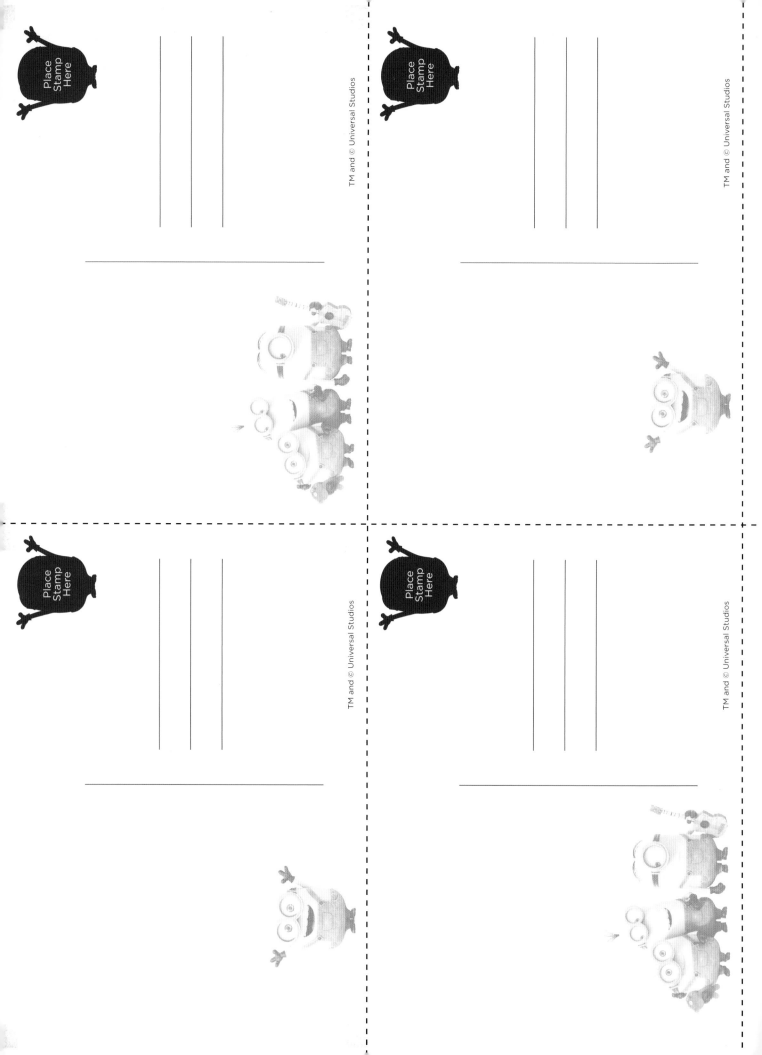

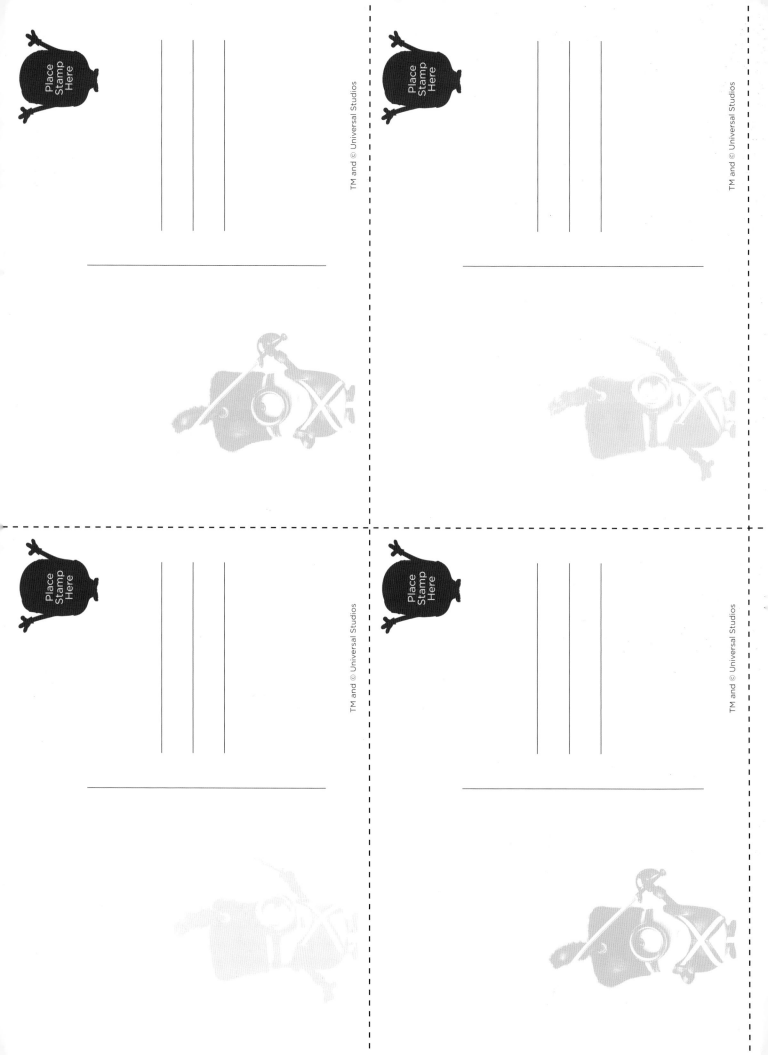

MINION
POLO ★ CLUB

KEEP CALM AND POTAKINO LO PATATA

TRANSLATION: YAY, EVIL

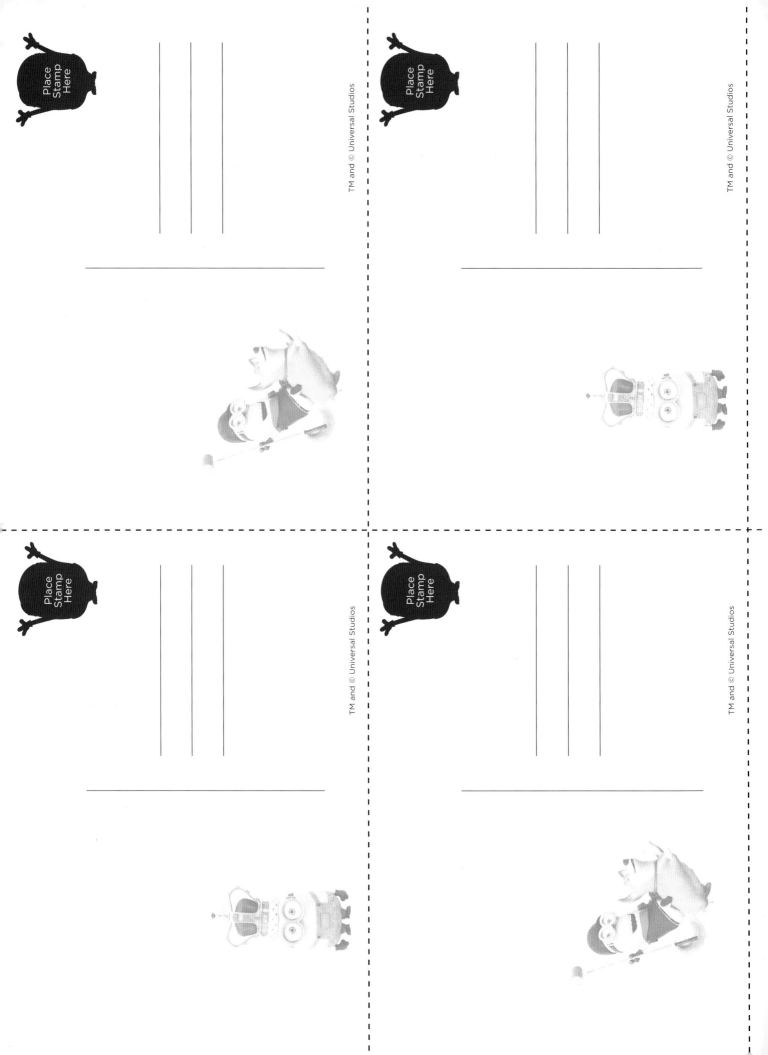

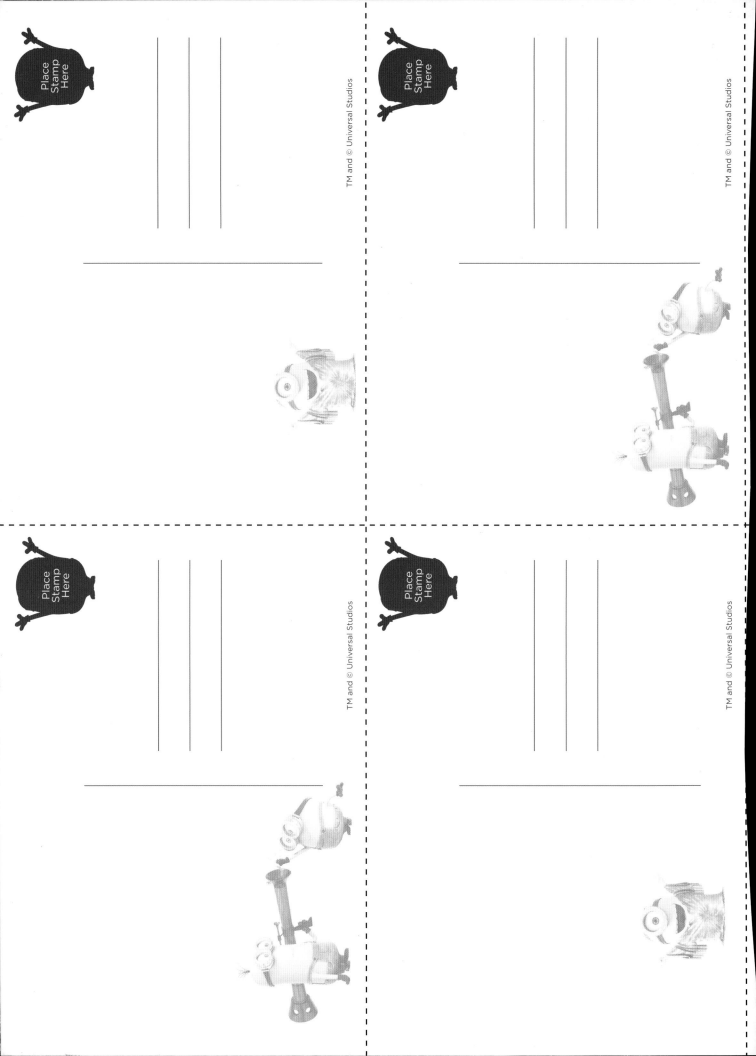